First published in Great Britain 2020 by Farshore
This edition published 2021 by Dean
An imprint of HarperCollins*Publishers*
1 London Bridge Street, London SE1 9GF
www.farshore.co.uk

HarperCollins*Publishers*
1st Floor, Watermarque Building, Ringsend Road
Dublin 4, Ireland

Written by Craig Jelley
Illustrated by Gregory Sokol
Cover Design by Maddox Philpot

ISBN 978 0 0085 0761 9
Printed and Bound in the UK using 100% Renewable Electricity at CPI Group (UK) Ltd
001

A CIP catalogue record for this title is available from the British Library.

MIX
Paper from
responsible sources
FSC™ C007454

This book is produced from independently certified FSC™ paper
to ensure responsible forest management.

For more information visit: www.harpercollins.co.uk/green

POKéMON™
MINI MAZES

Help Pikachu dodge through Flareon's flaming attack.

Start

- - → finish

5

Find a way through the maze to lead Ash to the city.

Finish

Start

Charjabugs store electricity that Trainers
can use to top up their gadgets' power.
Bring this one out of the maze.

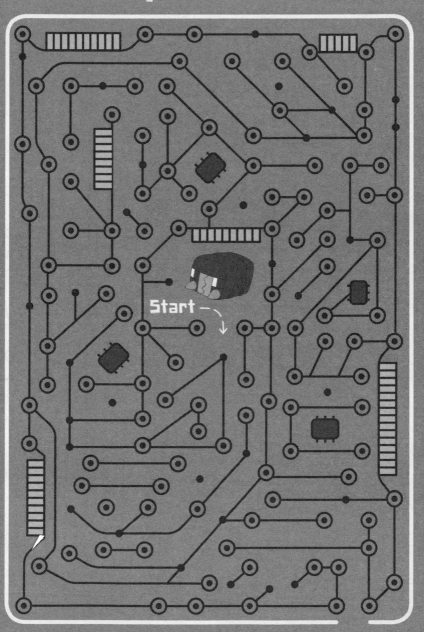

Start —

Finish

Start

Beware the Bewear. Follow the tracks
to see where it came from.

Finish

8

Start

Clefairy has been dancing in the moonlight, but needs to find a way home.

Finish

Start

This Crabrawler is looking for a way out of the sandy beach.

Comfey is collecting flowers to add to its vine. Help it pick up all the loose flowers around the maze.

Start

Finish

Start

Finish

You can tell a Litten has been
walking around here because
of the blaze it's left behind.

Start

This Cutiefly is
searching the flower
patch for nectar. Help
it navigate through
every flower.

finish

Froslass lives in icy caves deep inside the snowy mountains.

Start

Finish

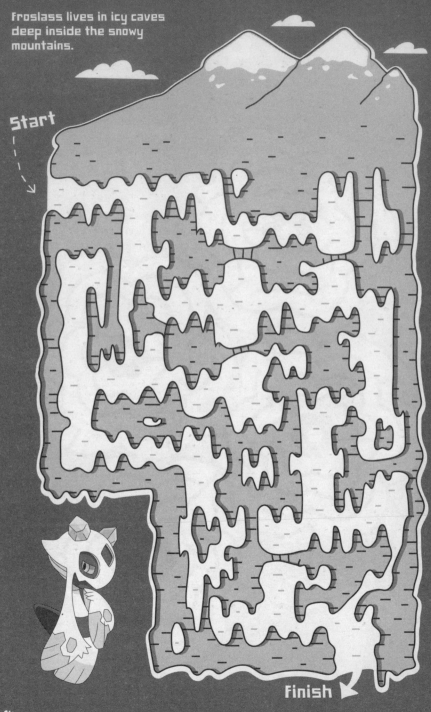

Finish

Start

Goomy needs to find a damp,
shaded cave to keep cool in.

Start - - - ⟶

Pikachu should have the element advantage over this brave Vaporeon. Dodge its water attack.

Finish

Komalas are rarely awake, but when they are, they love to clamp on to a tree trunk. Help this one reach the highest point in the forest.

Finish

Start

18

Can you see a route through the whirlpools that this Lapras can follow?

Start

Lugia soars high above
the clouds. Help it find a way
beneath the gathering storm.

Finish

The Alolan Marowak flings a deadly flaming bone. See if you can dodge the flames.

Start

Finish

Finish

Start

This Pikipek has drilled its home in a giant oak tree.
Help it find its way up to a perch.

Ever wondered what the world looks like through the eyes of a Sableye?

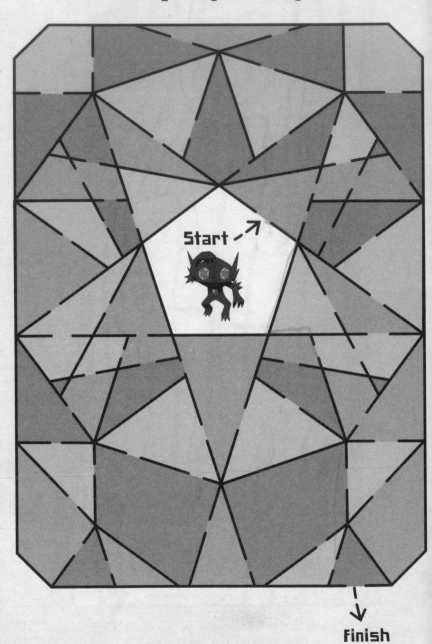

Start ↗

Finish ↓

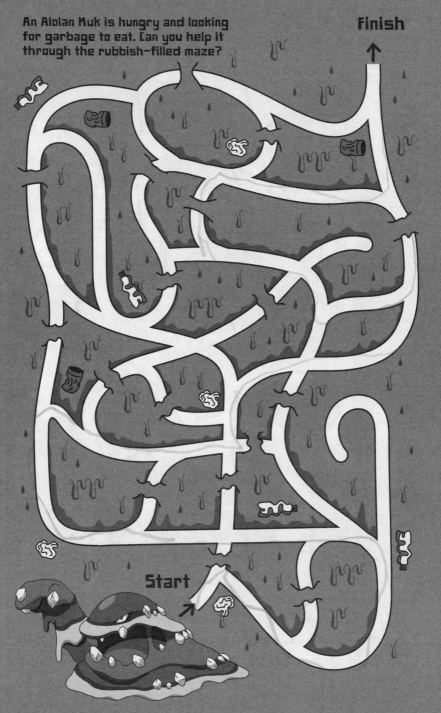

An Alolan Muk is hungry and looking for garbage to eat. Can you help it through the rubbish-filled maze?

Finish

Start

Start

Rotom Dex is excited to catalog all the Alolan Pokémon variants. Help him around the island to scan all the Pokémon along the way.

Finish

27

Start

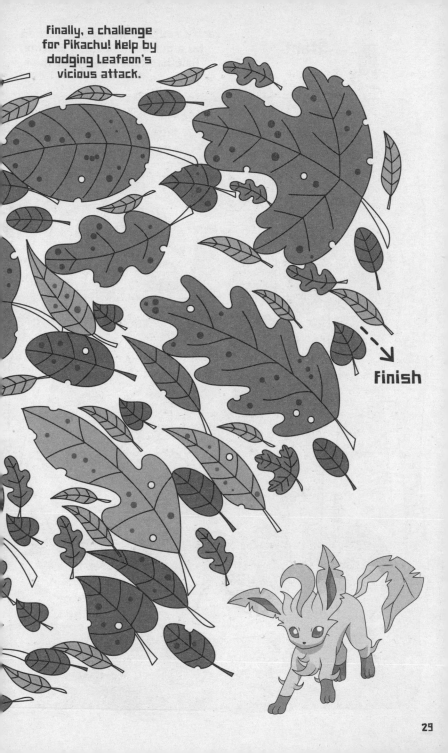

Finally, a challenge for Pikachu! Help by dodging Leafeon's vicious attack.

finish

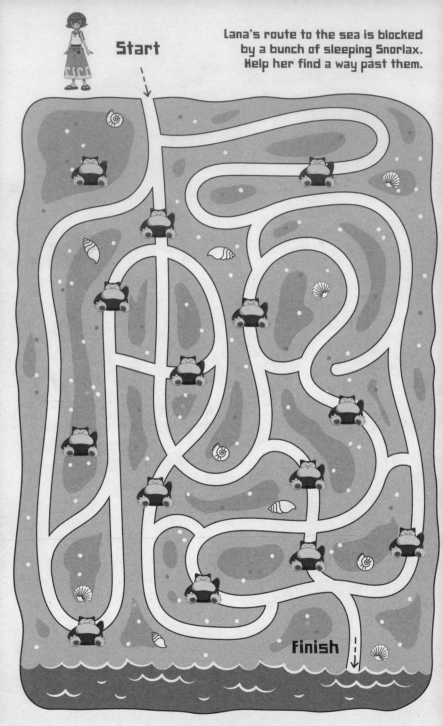

Start

Lana's route to the sea is blocked
by a bunch of sleeping Snorlax.
Help her find a way past them.

Finish

Finish

Salandit is kicking up a
cloud of dust. Can you
help Bounsweet escape
before the Salandit
strikes?

Start

find a route to see the Palossand, but don't get too close!

Finish

Start

33

Start

Help Rowlet find somewhere to rest and recharge during the day.

Finish

The Alolan Sandshrew loves nothing more than sliding round on its belly. See if you can help this one navigate the icy maze.

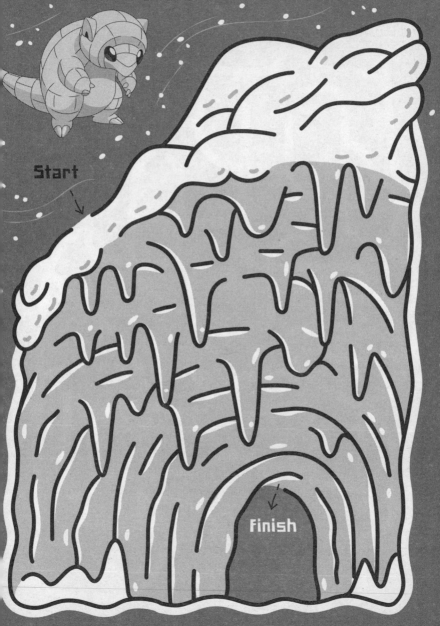

Start

Finish

According to legend, having
a Snorunt in your house is
good luck. Help this ice-type
Pokémon find a new home.

Start

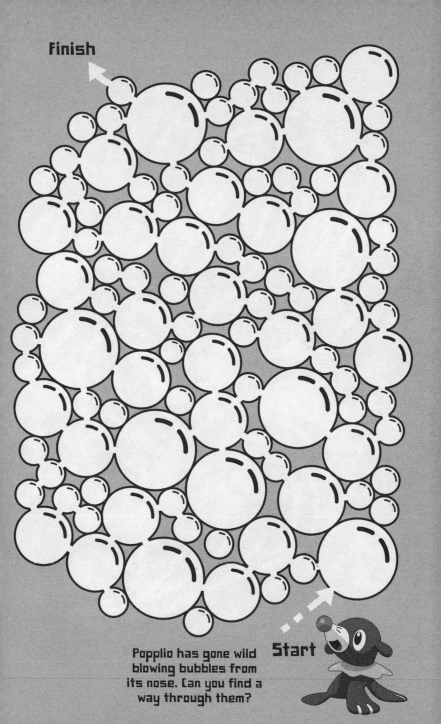

Finish

Start

Popplio has gone wild
blowing bubbles from
its nose. Can you find a
way through them?

Surf's up for this Alolan Raichu!

Start

Finish

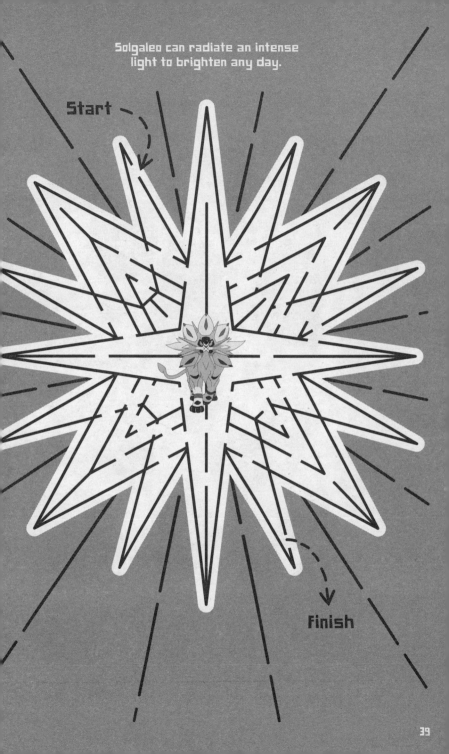

Solgaleo can radiate an intense
light to brighten any day.

Start

Finish

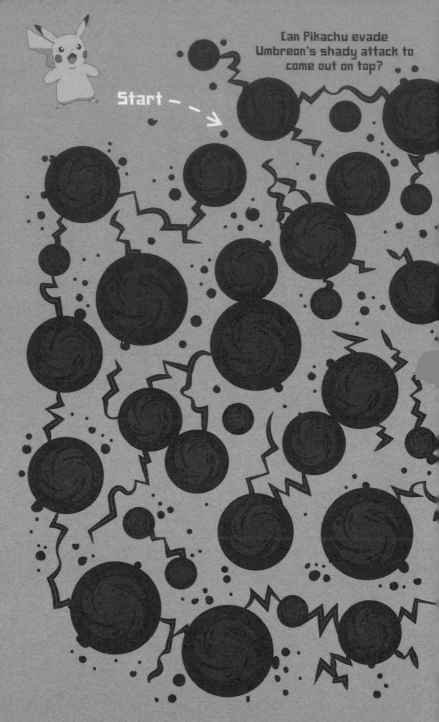

Can Pikachu evade Umbreon's shady attack to come out on top?

Start - - →

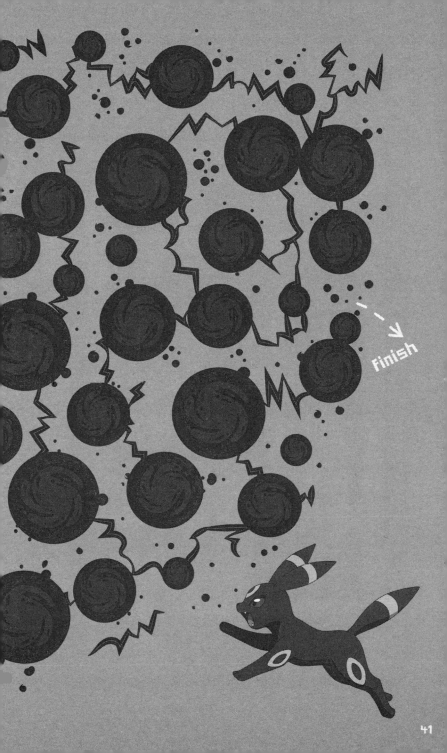

finish

Munchlax is looking for food to stash under its long fur. Help it pick up all the berries along this route.

Start

Finish

Atop a tall mountain, there's a sleepy Drampa resting. Find the route down.

Start

Finish

43

There's a huge ice cliff in Popplio's route, so it dives under the water to bypass it.

Start

Finish

finish ←

This brutal Sharpedo is zooming around to find a way out of the shipwreck. Can you help it?

Start →

Finish

Start

Gumshoos lives in a warren of tunnels where it sleeps during the day.

Ash uses dozens of Pokéballs
to catch his Pokémon friends.

Help Sneasel navigate
through the trees.

Start

Finish ↓

49

Which nectar is hidden in this maze?
Find a route from the nectar to find out
which style Oricorio has adopted.

Start

Pikachu is going head-to-head with Sylveon.

Finish

Start

Tapu Koko draws its power from the thunderclouds it gathers over Melemele island.

Start

Finish

The Alola region is dotted with bubbling volcanoes.

Start

Finish

Start

Espeon is ready to battle. Can you see which Pokémon it's attacking?

Start ↓

Team Rocket think they've
finally got their hands on
Pikachu ... something isn't
quite right though.

→ Finish

Can you stop yourself falling asleep from Jigglypuff's lullaby?

Start!

Finish

Rampardos has been rampaging through this building. Can you work out the route it took?

Start

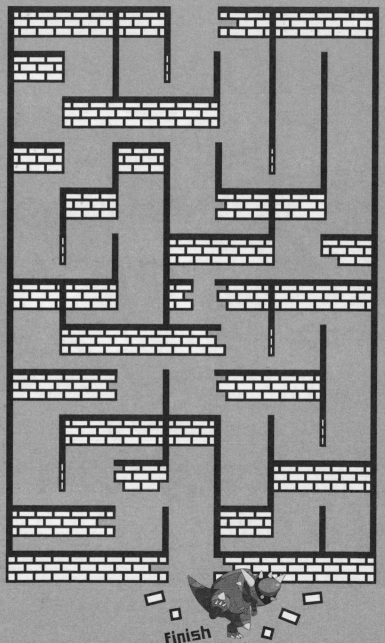

Finish

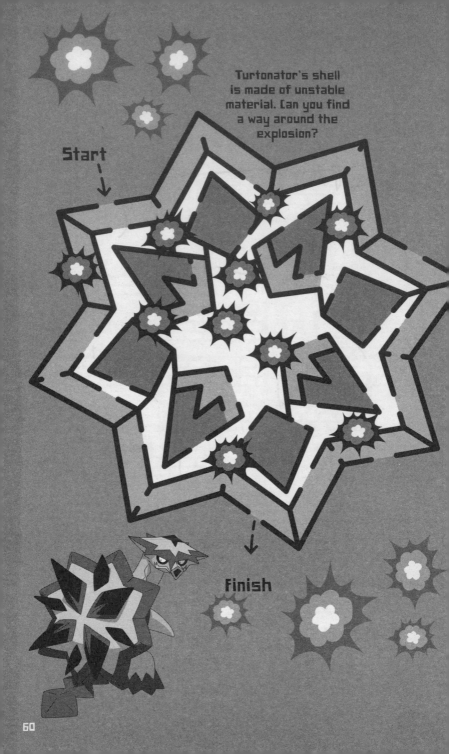

Turtonator's shell is made of unstable material. Can you find a way around the explosion?

Start

Finish

This Ledyba is taking a detour through the freshly-mown grass.

Start

finish

Start

It's a battle of the Electric-type Pokémon as Pikachu faces Jolteon.

finish

Mudbray is sliding down a muddy hill to coat its hooves.

Start

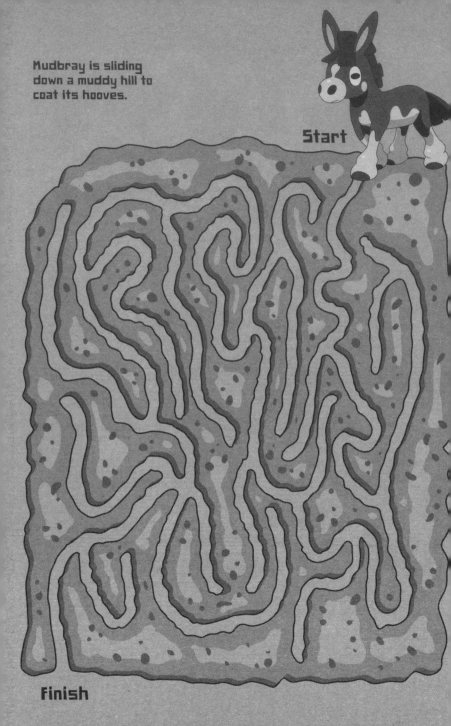

Finish

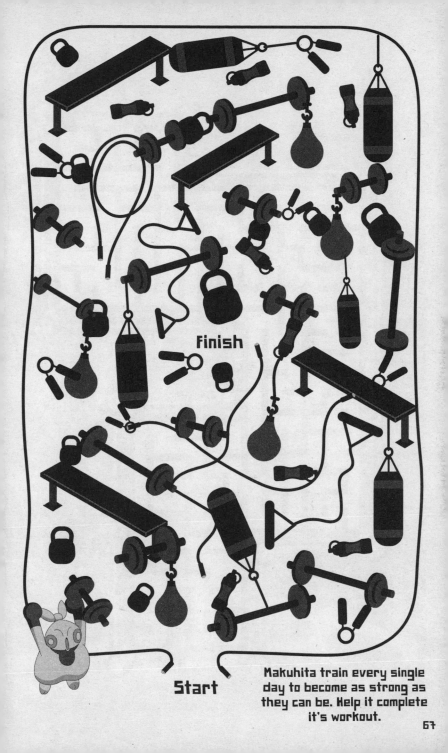

Finish

Start

Makuhita train every single
day to become as strong as
they can be. Help it complete
it's workout.

67

Oh, no. Magikarp has flailed out of the water again. Help it find its way back home.

Start

Finish

68

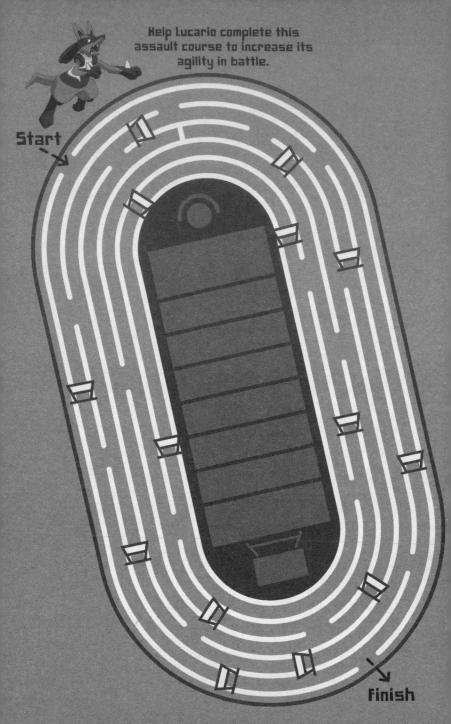

Help Lucario complete this assault course to increase its agility in battle.

Start

finish

70

Start

The Alolan Vulpix
sprays itself with
ice crystals if it
gets too hot.
Help it cool down.

finish

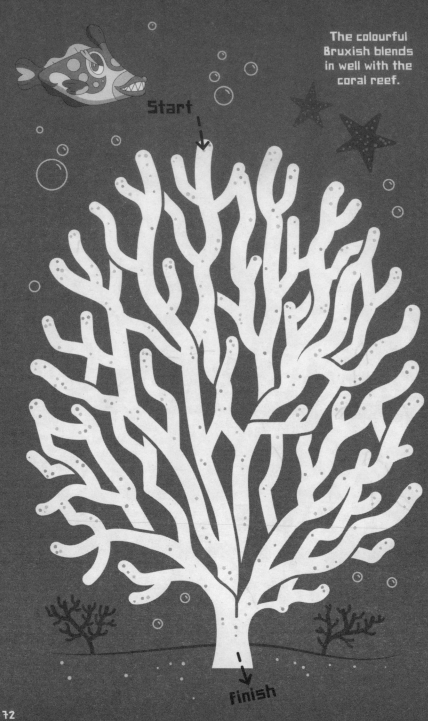

The colourful Bruxish blends in well with the coral reef.

Start

finish

Start

There are dozens of berries available on the Alola islands. See if you can work your way through them.

Finish

Pikachu's final battle against the Eevee Evolutions is versus Espeon, the psychic Pokémon. Head to the showdown!

Start

Finish

Solutions

Here are some answers for the mazes in the book.
The ultimate Trainers among you may have found
other solutions – good job!

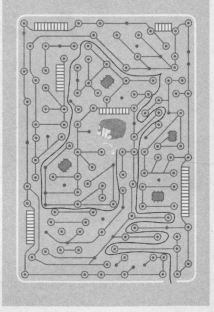

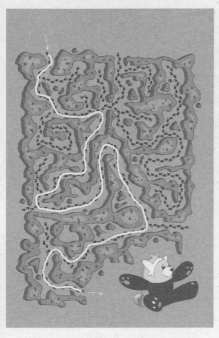

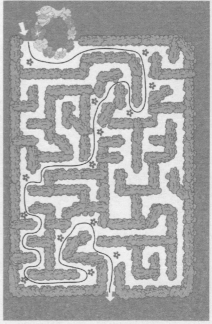

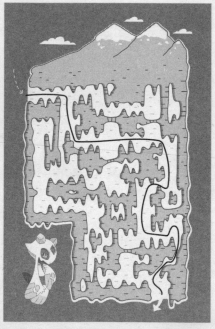

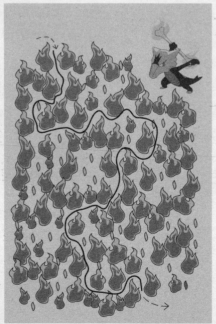

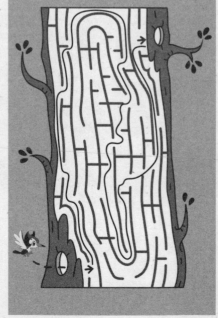

Answers - pages 24-27

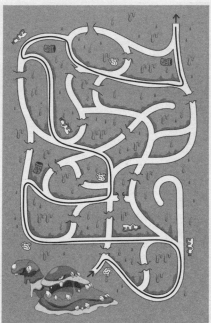

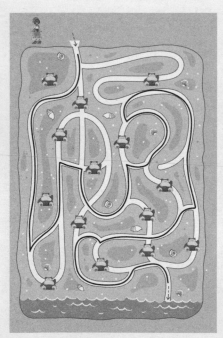

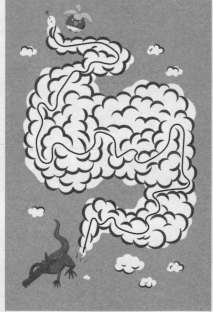

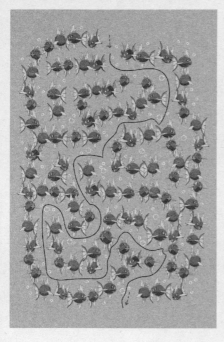

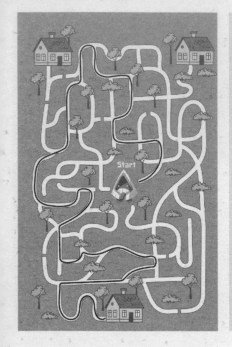

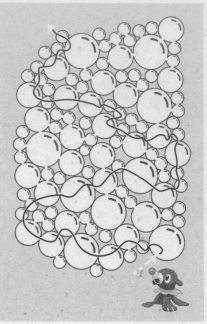

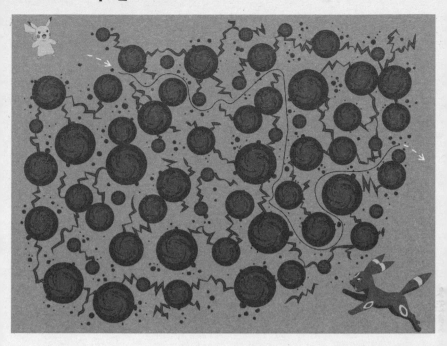

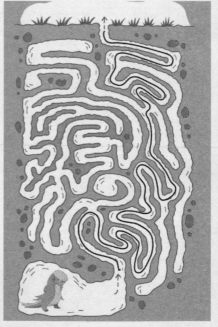

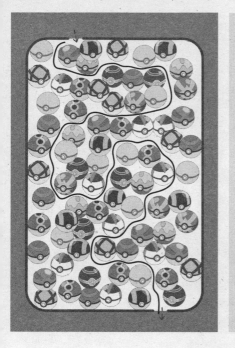

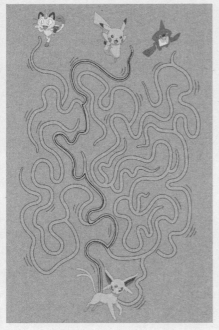

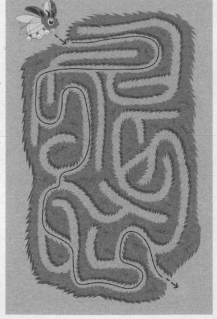

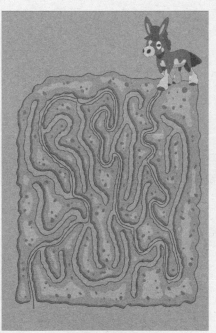

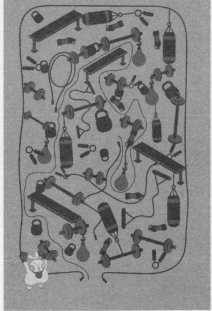

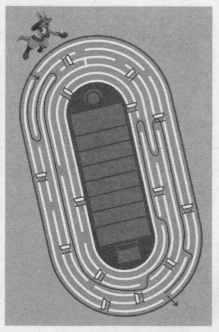

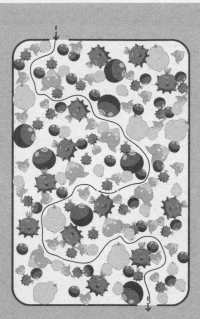